TAMBOURINE

Developed by the Center for Music and Young Children®

Kenneth K. Guilmartin
Founder/Director
Center for Music and Young Children
Princeton, New Jersey

Lili M. Levinowitz, Ph.D.
Professor of Music Education
Rowan University
Glassboro, New Jersey

AUTHORS

Kenneth K. Guilmartin conceived and led the development of the innovative Music Together program for the Center for Music and Young Children, which he founded in 1985. He has composed numerous scores for off-Broadway and regional theatre productions and is a popular presenter at early childhood and music educator conferences. He has created music programs and conducted teacher trainings for early childhood centers nationwide. A graduate of Swarthmore College, he studied composition and pedagogy at Manhattan School of Music and is certified in Dalcroze Eurhythmics by the Manhattan Dalcroze Institute.

Lili M. Levinowitz, Ph.D., is Professor of Music Education at Rowan University. She is a national authority on early childhood music and is actively involved in teaching very young children as well as graduate students. Her articles appear frequently in professional journals and popular magazines. She received her Ph.D. from Temple University where she was director of the Children's Music Development Program.

The authors gratefully acknowledge Lyn Ransom, D.M.A., Director of Program Development at the Center for Music and Young Children, for her contributions to this book as a curriculum consultant and writer.

The Center for Music and Young Children® (CMYC), developer of Music Together, was founded in 1985. CMYC is committed to helping families, caregivers, and early childhood professionals rediscover the pleasure and educational value of informal musical experiences. Rather than emphasizing traditional music performances, CMYC encourages family participation in spontaneous musical activity occurring within the context of daily life. CMYC recognizes that all children are musical and that every child needs a stimulating, supportive music environment to achieve basic competence in the wonderful human capacity for music-making.

Music Together is a music and movement approach to early childhood music development for infant, toddler, preschool, and kindergarten children and their parents, teachers, and other primary caregivers. Originally offered to the public in 1987, it pioneered the concept of a research-based, developmentally appropriate early childhood music curriculum that strongly emphasizes and facilitates adult involvement.

The Music Together approach develops every child's birthright of basic music competence by encouraging the actual experiencing of music rather than the learning of concepts or information about music. Music Together began as an educational project of the Center for Music and Young Children and is now enjoyed by thousands of families in the United States and abroad.

For further information about Music Together programs, teacher training, parent education, child-friendly instruments, or classes, both national and international, please contact us.

Music Together LLC
Princeton, New Jersey
(800) 728-2692
www.musictogether.com

CONTENTS

Read more about FSC Certification
on the inside back cover.

MAKING THE MOST OF YOUR CLASS EXPERIENCE

Reading this preface will help you maximize your class experience. We will discuss the basic Music Together philosophy, how children learn, what parents can do in class, how to use the recording and songbook (even if you don't read music), and how to start making music at home.

Not every parent feels comfortable in class at first. You may have had a difficult time with music or music lessons as a child, or you may have grown up with no music in your life. In spite of your own past experiences, you have taken a major musical step for your child by enrolling in this class. We invite you to be childlike again and to experience music as if it were new to you. Forget your images of perfect performances and music for the talented few—we'll help you find ways to enjoy music so your child will catch your spirit and enjoy it, too.

Brothers and sisters can attend class together. One of the goals of Music Together is to bring music back to family life. Can you imagine sitting around as a family and singing instead of watching TV or playing computer games? As technology increases, the importance of non-technical group interaction also increases, especially at home. We think that family music-making can be a wonderful activity shared by brothers, sisters, parents, relatives, and even nannies. For this reason, siblings are encouraged to attend class together, so that they will experience the same music and movement activities and will want to recreate them at home together.

Classes with children of many ages are educationally sound. The younger children learn by observing and imitating the older ones; the older children benefit from singing to, moving with, and being appreciated by the younger ones. Most importantly, vocal discoveries, movement ideas, or ways to play an instrument are communicated freely from child to child, regardless of age or stage of development. Leading child psychologists endorse mixed-age groupings because children learn more easily and more deeply there than in single-age classes.

It is never too early or too late to begin Music Together classes. In class you will experience music that is fun, accessible, and sophisticated, so that people of many ages can enjoy it. Because adults and children enter the experience at many different levels, each person comes away with what he needs for his own musical growth. It is like a musical buffet: each person picks his or her favorite foods today, but may choose something different tomorrow, depending upon tastes and the nourishment needed. A toddler, an infant, or a four-year-old may take different things home from a Music Together class, but each will find many things that meet his or her needs on any given day. In this way, a child may begin classes at any age and will continue to grow musically throughout succeeding semesters.

When possible, we encourage parents to enroll children in Music Together as newborns. Babies are especially receptive to sounds, perhaps even more than to what they see. Infancy is an excellent time for a child to learn music, because infants expand their tonal vocabulary rapidly. Because they learn so fast, we encourage parents to bring babies to mixed-age classes with their older siblings or to enroll in a Music Together Babies Class (for eight-month-olds or younger). If you or your friends have an infant, please consider enrolling in this class if it is offered in your area.

A CHILD'S WISH LIST

I wish you would sing to me all day long. I want you to put your face close to mine and look into my eyes and sing with a mouth that's big and expressive. I hope you will also hold me and dance and tap lightly on my arms and legs. I want this sweet rhythmic movement several times a day. I'm an infant.

I want you to sing and play musically while you change my diaper, while we ride in the car, while you dance with me, when we go for a walk, when we take a bath. I love the stuff of music—the red drum, the sound from the speakers, the songs with silly sneezes and funny movements. I love to dance up and down when I hear music! I love being swung to slow music or bounced to fast music or danced with in a circle. I'm a toddler.

I wish I could do it myself, and I can. I can remember the words to songs—the tune, too. I can enter my own world and sing to myself for hours or play in my own one-person band. I like the way I make music, I like to watch others make music, and I'd like to do some of the things the music teacher does. I really love it when my family will dance and play instruments with me. I'm a three-year-old.

Music is one of my specialties. I love learning exactly how to do a clapping pattern or a dance step. I like to play instruments the real way. I love to practice the things I'm interested in, and I know when I get things "right" according to me. I'm attracted to other kids who can do great things in music, and I'm beginning to feel like I need music every day and maybe for the rest of my life. I'm four-and-a-half, and proud of it!

YOU AND YOUR CHILD CAN LEARN MUSIC!

How do people learn music? How do infants learn? Toddlers? Four-year-olds? Early childhood experts believe that each child learns from rich and varied music experiences and that, given a variety of engaging activities, each child will learn the things she is ready to learn at any given moment. This approach, which is often called "developmentally appropriate practice," allows each child to be responsible for his own learning and helps adults view children's growth through stages of development, not ages.

Children learn through play. Your child may want to listen, move, sing, or play an instrument at home, sometimes for extended periods of time. The child is recalling, recounting, experimenting, practicing, and creating through play. Sometimes he will want to play alone, and sometimes, more than anything else, he will want you to join him. Take your cues from your child and see what happens!

Here are the four basic ideas of the Music Together philosophy. You can read more about these ideas in the parent guide, and you may discuss them briefly in class and at parent education evenings.

- All children are musical.
- All children can achieve basic music competence.
- The participation and modeling of parents and caregivers is essential to a child's music growth.
- Young children's musical growth occurs best in a playful, musically rich, and developmentally appropriate setting, free of direct instruction and performance pressure, where learning activities are accessible, interesting, and fun for both children and adults.

All children are musical.

You may be reassured to know that all children are musical and that all adults are, too! You don't need to wonder if your child has musical talent: all children do. You needn't wonder if you have any musical talent: you do! It may be resting there, undiscovered and unused, but it's there. Music Together classes can help you develop your talent, as well as your child's.

In Western culture, we tend to believe that musical talent or aptitude is given to only a few. We tend to believe that these "talented" people are the ones who grow up to be rock stars, symphony orchestra players, or concert pianists. In actual fact, music apti-

tude or talent is normally distributed in a "bell curve" manner, that is, music aptitude is distributed throughout the population just as talent in language, math, visual art, architecture, computer engineering, dance, and other areas are. In fact, eighty-four percent of the population is born with enough music aptitude to play in a symphony orchestra, and only two percent of the population is born with either exceptionally high or low music intelligence.

So, despite your fears that either you or your child may not have any musical talent, rest assured that all of you have some level of music aptitude. You will be in a class where your aptitude will be exercised and your child's will be nurtured.

To learn more about this, you can read Edwin Gordon's work on music aptitude or Howard Gardner's theories of multiple intelligences. These are referenced in the back of this book, along with other publications of interest.

All children can achieve basic music competence.

Music Together defines basic music competence in very simple terms. A child is musically competent when he or she can sing in tune with accurate rhythm.

This sounds basic—everyone should be able to carry a tune, right? Do an experiment: think of six friends and write down the names. Now check off the ones that you know who can carry a tune by themselves, without a radio, CD, or keyboard. You may find that one or none out of six can sing. In the general population in the US, fewer and fewer people can carry a tune or keep a beat now, even though they once had the potential to do so. This is unfortunate since all children have musical talent or aptitude and all children can achieve this skill.

If your child experiences interesting music in class and experiments with that music at home for several years during early childhood, he or she is more likely to achieve basic music competence by the age of three or four. This is an astounding statement, although it sounds simple. By age three or four, children who have had enough early music experience can usually sing in tune with accurate rhythm. This means that these children can sing and keep a beat as well or better than much of the adult population! Given early exposure to good musical models, it is completely

rmal for young children to sing, create songs, move rhythmical- play instruments in a steady tempo, feel at home with unusual eters, improvise rhythmically, and enjoy music-making.

your child has active experience with a wealth of interesting ngs and rhythmic movement before the age of five, he or she is ely to have an excellent music and movement vocabulary for e rest of his or her life. If a child has less experience in music, d therefore less opportunity to experiment with it, he may ach basic music competence at age five or six, but it could be as te as third grade, or never. Some children never achieve basic usic competence because they have had inadequate experience music. This is becoming more and more common as music-aking becomes less important in our culture and family life. The chness, variety, and amount of your child's early experience in usic affects both what he achieves and the delight he derives.

nal competence. You can watch your child develop and notice hen she can sing an entire song with the correct melody. When child can sing the melody beginning on different notes, that is, hen the child can maintain the melodic patterns even though the y is changed, we know that the child is competent in melody. She n hear the melody in her mind and can think flexibly about the nal patterns of the tune. She can remember and recall a tune in der to play it or to make up new words to it. This inner hearing ility is key to making music, both alone and in groups, and will lp your child considerably if she begins to study an instrument.

ythm competence. You can also notice your child developing ythmically. When he can say a rhythmic chant correctly at fferent tempos or speeds, then we know he can maintain the ythmic patterns through his thought process, not just by rote emorization. This shows that he is competent in rhythm. When child is competent in both rhythm and melody, we say he has hieved basic music competence. While musical competence may difficult for many adults to achieve, it is *normal* for children ho have had early childhood music experiences. You are to be ngratulated for providing music-making experiences for your ild when he is most ready to learn.

sually a child becomes competent in one area several months or en years earlier than in the other. Researchers have noted that ost people have an affinity for either pitch or rhythm and may hieve competence in one area sooner than the other. Children

who love to move and who respond to music by dancing rather than singing may be more attracted to the rhythmic aspects of music. Young children who respond to music more by singing along, listening intently, or playing an instrument may be more melodic or tonal in nature.

Do you think your child is more attracted to rhythm or pitch? You may want to write down what you notice on the page entitled "Musical Memories." When he is older, he will be very interested in your memories of his musical experiences as a child.

While many children and adults may have a stronger affinity for either melody or rhythm, some have an equal attraction to both. It's like walking and talking. Some children start to do both at once; others develop one skill sooner than the other. Both are interesting for parents to notice, but neither predicts how well a child will walk, talk, or make music as an adult.

The participation and modeling of parents and care-givers is essential to a child's musical growth.

You may not believe this, but it is true. The parent or primary caregiver is the child's most important music teacher! It is the parent or caregiver alone that can teach a young child to enjoy music-making. A music teacher can help your child learn skills and content, but only you can help your child enjoy music. The reason for this is simple. Young children naturally want to be like their parents and enjoy the same things they do—if the parents swim, the children will; if the parents read, the children will; if the parents make music, the children will, too.

You may not want the responsibility of being your child's most important musical influence, but remember, the Music Together teacher leads the songs, provides opportunities to learn skills, and helps you figure out what to do. All you have to do is enjoy music and movement and communicate that in simple, direct ways to your child. Then, because music is such a strong form of commu-nication, you will not need to tell your child, "I just love making music. Look at how much fun it is for me to play a shaker and sing!" Your child will sense that from feeling your body move and hearing you sing in whatever voice you have. Music can be one of the most wonderful nonverbal means of communication that you will experience together.

In this songbook, you will read about a child's wish list for music class and the parent's path for helping them. Enjoy these lists, then think about your child. Perhaps you would like to rewrite the music wish list from your own child's point of view. What do you think she would like you to do?

Young children's musical growth occurs best in a playful, musically rich, and developmentally appropriate setting.

This setting for your child is free of direct instruction and performance pressure. Learning activities are accessible, interesting and fun for both children and adults. In class, you will notice that there is a good deal of childlike play. This is because children learn through play and experimentation. In class you will experience music, rather than learn facts about it. You will be invited to participate in musicmaking, from simply keeping a beat with egg shakers to improvising rhythms in the play-along. This playful music participation is the opposite of performance pressure—there are no performance rules or expectations. You and your child will be encouraged to enter into activities at your own comfort level and participate freely.

THE PARENT'S PATH

In class, join in the singing without judging your participation. Even if you feel shy or hesitant or musically inexperienced, find a way to relax and enjoy singing the songs. Your child will know if you genuinely enjoy making music, so find a way that works authentically for you.

Join in the moving and dancing activities in class, and share that enjoyment physically with your child. He will understand that moving is fun and a good thing to do when he sees you swaying, clapping, stomping, rocking, and jumping.

Take cues from your child and respond musically. If your child "coos" on a pitch, return the sound. If your child sings on the way to the grocery store, sing with her. If your child asks for the Music Together recording and brings an instrument to you, try to stop what you are doing and play with your child.

Respond to your child in nonverbal ways. That is, respond musically without talking, so your child will grow in his music experience and will understand that you enjoy music communication and play. Look at him when you sing together, join in his beat on the drum, or imitate his "dance." You might even smile at your child when you do something really silly to let him know that you're just playing and having fun.

As your familiarity with the program grows, you may want to refer back to the four concepts just discussed: All children are musical. All children can achieve basic music competence The participation and modeling of parents and caregivers is essential to a child's musical growth. Young children's musical growth occurs best in a playful, musically rich, and developmentally appropriate setting, free of direct instruction and performance pressure, where learning activities are accessible, interesting, and fun for both children and adults.

We invite you to share any music, dance, or movement skills you have with the class In most families, the child is happy that the parent can contribute something special to class activities. If you have an instrument, bring it, especially for the play-along. If you have a beautiful voice and can hear harmonies, sing out freely. If you have a background in dance, improvise at your own level in class, and others will learn from you.

Move to music, play instruments, and sing at home often. You are the real teacher for your child's enjoyment of music, so plan to make music together several times during the week. Some families make music after breakfast every Saturday morning. Others sing and play instruments just after supper. Others keep a basket of instruments and the songbook in the car for making music on trips. Use the songbook and recording to stimulate family music-making. Play and experiment together often and see what happens.

Your child may sometimes want to absorb the activity without participating: this is expected. You may want to participate quietly at first, and this is also fine. The actual activities are designed to be interesting to adults and children alike, and they provide for many levels of participation.

SPECIAL SETTINGS

Nannies. Many families send their primary daytime caregiver to class with their child. Some nannies are very comfortable with music-making and use the Music Together activities to enliven the child's time at home. Other nannies are less comfortable with music-making, and may need some direction from you. Try to imagine the questions she could ask. What is expected of me in a music class? Do I have to be responsible for anything in particular in the class? At home? How am I supposed to use the songbook? The recording? You may want to give the nanny specific assignments, for example, to play with music and your child every day for at least a half-hour. Invite her to read the introduction to this book, and ask her to report back to you on the child's actions during class. It may take a few months to help the nanny feel comfortable singing, dancing, creating, observing, and playing in class and at home, but what a wonderful and valuable use of the time she and your child spend together. When there is a parent education evening or class you can attend, try to attend with the nanny so she can model her participation after yours.

Babysitters. These occasional caregivers are important to family life and may appreciate guidance. If you keep a book of notes and activity suggestions for babysitters, be sure to write about the Music Together CD, songbook, and activities. You might suggest that the babysitter try at least three or four music activities each time he or she stays with your child. The simple instructions written under each song will be a good guide. When you return home, ask the babysitter about the music activities and how your child children responded.

Older children. In school and out of school, parents and teachers report that these songs are among the favorites of children through third grade and higher.

Older adults. Because the songs in this collection are accessible but sophisticated, they appeal to people of many ages. Grandparents and caregivers may find a new joy in life when they discover how much fun it is to sing and dance with their little ones! However, grandparents may tend to instruct children as they were instructed in grade school. You may need to explain current thinking in music development in order for them to relax, play, and have fun with music.

Individuals with special needs. Parents and teachers involved with Music Together recount story after story about the value of this music for inspiring joy and language. People with Alzheimer's disease often enjoy music, and the Music Together songs are often favorites. Many times people who have lost the ability to speak can nevertheless sing the texts to songs. In addition, children with special needs often find the activities engaging. Music Together recordings won't provide a cure, but they can provide hours of happiness, music-making, and family comfort for people of all ages.

Preschool and childcare. In many communities, Music Together is a vital part of preschool programs, and children participate in regular music classes as part of their daily routine. Parents receive materials to take home, so that they can make music with their children, whether or not they are able to visit the daytime classes. In addition, the Music Together specialist, along with the supporting materials, help teachers and aides to understand and facilitate the process of music development. Current research continues to confirm that music activities can play a powerful role in a child's development. When it is time for you to choose a preschool or childcare center, be sure to ask about its music program.

Family reunions. Many families get together regularly with aunts, uncles, grandparents, new babies, and lots of cousins. Why not bring a Music Together CD or songbook and lead some family activities? Let your children choose the songs or dances they especially enjoy, and encourage teenagers or older children to help the little ones. If you join in, leading gently when necessary, other children and parents will feel comfortable participating. You might begin the sing-along with songs you think the extended family might know; then move to less familiar songs. If you take a basket of instruments and end with a play-along, you'll be making many children happy. Encourage the grandparents, especially, to join the music-making. They generally love to watch children and are often very spontaneous in the way they make music. A child may want to be the Music Together teacher and direct the class. Won't it be fun to be the student?

HOW TO USE THIS BOOK

This book will be a wonderful resource for you. You can use it to help you recall activities from class or to remember the words to songs. Take some time to put the recording on and follow the words as you hear the songs, so you can become familiar with the music. Glance over the activity suggestions as you listen.

If you don't read music, use the book occasionally to point out words or pictures to your child as you sing or hear them. Over time, both of you will make connections between the notes on the page and the notes you hear. You may notice that music notes sometimes appear in a child's drawings just like other symbols in a child's life, like the "ABCs." Parents who play instruments "by ear" may find that using the book to follow or remember the music will help them play better and understand more.

If you do read music, you will enjoy playing or singing through the collection. Parents who used to play when they were younger may delight in taking a forgotten instrument out of the case and playing through the songs. Your child will notice that you read the music and play your instrument and might be interested in doing the same thing. Parents and caregivers who do read music will be able to play along either with or in place of the recording.

Try out the family activities you can do at home. Each music page contains several ideas for interacting with your child. Many of these ideas will be familiar to you from class, but some will be new and especially fun to try at home. Some activity suggestions are for a particular age group, others are for a setting, others are designed to inspire movement or instrument play. Experiment with these suggestions. Jot down what your child liked and write in other ideas you think of, so your songbook becomes a recipe book for a good family time.

Listen for featured instruments on the recording. In the colored sidebar, there are drawings of instruments featured on the recording. When you look at the book with an older child, point out the instruments as you hear them on the recording. If the featured instrument is one which a child could manage safely and enjoyably, try to provide it, so she can play along at home.

Play "found" and real instruments with the recording. You may want to collect some household objects that make sounds and keep them handy in a basket or drawer so they can come out easily for music-making. Play them often, both with the recording and without. Parents who play instruments will be especially at home with the play-along, in which everyone improvises at his

own level, both children and adults. Portable instruments like the guitar, clarinet, or harmonica can go on family outings and help you make music anywhere, any time. To order instruments that are well constructed, nontoxic, and child-friendly, please visit our online store at www.musictogether.com.

Look at the songbook illustrations with your child. You will notice that several songs are illustrated with beautiful woodcuts. Take time to look at these with your child and let her take the lead in pointing out what she sees. Sing the song while you look at the picture, and enjoy the richness of visual art and music combined. Many songs do not have illustrations, so this makes a perfect opportunity for your child to draw or paint something. Older children may enjoy hanging their pictures or collecting them in a personal songbook.

Use the songbook as a storybook. It is especially nice to use the Music Together songbooks at bedtime or naptime. The songs and pictures may remind the child of pleasurable experiences with you, helping him to fall asleep easily. The routine quiet of nap or bed may make the child receptive to your singing the lullabies or songs, so put aside your own opinion of your voice for a moment and sing to your young child with the sweetest voice she knows!

HOW TO REACH US

Your Music Together center director or teacher has been trained in children's music learning from birth to age five. Take time to think about music development questions you would like to discuss, and ask your teacher before or after class.

You may also contact the Center for Music and Young Children directly. To find out about classes for friends or relatives in other states or to discuss doing special projects with us, please call or visit our website. We are especially interested in knowing how Music Together classes help your children enjoy and learn music both now and as they mature. We also value knowing how the program helps or inspires your family to make music, so do write and tell us! We would enjoy hearing from you.

Center for Music and Young Children
66 Witherspoon Street, Princeton NJ 08542
(800) 728-2692 • www.musictogether.com

SONG COLLECTIONS

At the core of the Music Together program are its nine song collections, each characterized by its own graphic, color, and instrument, and each including its own recording and activity songbook. These collections, designed to be used one per semester, are not sequential; so you can begin Music Together classes at any semester with any collection.

This semester you will take part in the rich and balanced music experiences of the current song collection. Then, next semester, you will receive a new songbook and recording and enjoy new songs, dances, and movement activities, while learning more about your child's musical growth and development. Your child will thrive on the continuity from class to class, and if you attend for three consecutive years, you will experience all nine song collections—what a wealth of music for your family to enjoy!

The music is pitched in just the right range for children's voices and includes songs, rhythmic chants, tonal and rhythm patterns, and instrumental play-alongs, all in a rich variety of tonalities and meters. Original songs and arrangements by the program coauthors make these collections unique. Outstanding instrumentalists play a variety of instruments, such as guitar, bass, flutes, keyboards, and percussion. And all of the songs are suitable for mixed-age groups, perfect for childcare centers or families with children of different ages.

Music Together's song collections are research-based and artistically conceived and produced. They are also classroom- and family-tested. Since 1987, the feedback of hundreds of teachers and thousands of families has been incorporated into these constantly evolving materials.

BONGOS   BELLS   TRIANGLE

FIDDLE   DRUM   TAMBOURINE

FLUTE   STICKS   MARACAS

Because the Music Together song collections are not sequential, you can begin your Music Together experience at any semester with any collection. The order of the collections is: Bongos, Bells, Triangle, Fiddle, Drum, Tambourine, Flute, Sticks, Maracas. In addition, some family-class centers offer summer classes using the Summer Songs 1, 2, and 3 anthologies, with songs drawn from the nine core collections.

*I*magine what your child experiences in a Music Together class! There are wonderful sounds, interesting movements, instruments to play, other children to watch, silly things to laugh at, an inviting teacher to follow, and music that your child loves! Your child is in class with you or the caregiver you select, and this grownup holds him, hugs him, sings, and loves making music, too! What a comfortable and exciting experience!

Going to Music Together can be wonderful for a parent, too. You may love the activities and love seeing your child's response. It is exceptionally satisfying for a parent to have found a program that allows his or her child to flourish! You will learn about music development in class, through special attention given to individual children. You will meet other adults and may even become a favorite grownup for another child. You will learn songs, movement activities, and dances which are fun in themselves and provide for family music-making at home.

One of the delights of becoming involved in Music Together is discovering or rediscovering your own relationship to music. You may discover that you love to sing, or you may find that the classes provide just the opportunity you need to get out an instrument you haven't played for years. Drumming or dancing may feel new and wonderful, especially removed from the anxieties of high school or college performance experiences. This musical awakening has happened for hundreds of parents who have found—or rediscovered—the great satisfaction and joy in making music with their children. Welcome!

Hello Song

K. Guilmartin

This catchy tune is a favorite, because children love musical play with names.

Sing the "Hello Song" using your child's name or the names of friends, relatives, pets, or dolls. As you sing, sway gently back and forth to the beat, so your child sees and feels the pulse. Sing this cheerful song as a ritual when you first see your child in the morning or any time you greet him.

Variations: Try using it as a peek-a-boo song, singing a phrase at a time as you pop out from behind a scarf, newspaper, or other object. Honor special visitors by singing them the "Hello Song," and incorporate it into special parties or family meals.

Older children will enjoy a "silly" version. For example, sing to various unlikely objects, such as the clock, the spoon, or your nose: "Hello, to my sneaker, so glad to see you!" Then you can get them to sing "hello" to other objects, by pointing to them during the song. Another good "silly" game is to sing the wrong names of family or friends. Make a mistake, then ask the children to show you how to do it right. Preschoolers love this!

Infants/toddlers: Babies are very focused on faces, especially mouths. So sing close to your baby, so he can feel your energy, sense the rhythm and your breathing, and see your facial expression. Hug your child and sway with her on your lap. Every time you greet each other after being apart, give your child some lap time and a few repetitions of this song. Rituals like this mean a lot to young children. They also help children grow musically, because musical expression becomes a natural part of daily life.

Recording: Guitar, bass, shaker, tambourine

Old Brass Wagon

Traditional, arranged and adapted
by K. Guilmartin and L. Levinowitz
Additional words by K. Guilmartin

Lively

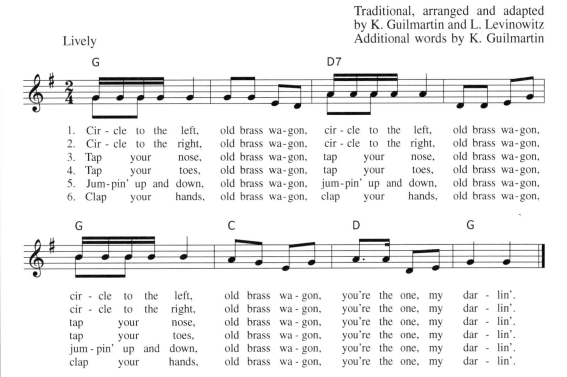

1. Cir - cle to the left, old brass wa-gon, cir - cle to the left, old brass wa-gon,
2. Cir - cle to the right, old brass wa-gon, cir - cle to the right, old brass wa-gon,
3. Tap your nose, old brass wa-gon, tap your nose, old brass wa-gon,
4. Tap your toes, old brass wa-gon, tap your toes, old brass wa-gon,
5. Jum-pin' up and down, old brass wa-gon, jum-pin' up and down, old brass wa-gon,
6. Clap your hands, old brass wa-gon, clap your hands, old brass wa-gon,

cir - cle to the left, old brass wa - gon, you're the one, my dar - lin'.
cir - cle to the right, old brass wa - gon, you're the one, my dar - lin'.
tap your nose, old brass wa - gon, you're the one, my dar - lin'.
tap your toes, old brass wa - gon, you're the one, my dar - lin'.
jum - pin' up and down, old brass wa - gon, you're the one, my dar - lin'.
clap your hands, old brass wa - gon, you're the one, my dar - lin'.

Put on the CD and get everyone in your family up on their feet! Sing along as you do the movements suggested on the recording—"circle to the left," "circle to the right," and so on. In the instrumental break, repeat these movements or improvise some of your own (see "large movement" below). When your family knows the song, sing and dance without the recording.

Lap song: Sing when your family is sitting around relaxing. Bounce babies and toddlers on your lap while you sing "bouncin' up and down." Play pat-a-cake with older children. Hug your child on the words "you're the one, my darlin'."

Songbook illustration: Ask you child what she sees in the picture, then sing her answer. For example, "Go for a ride, old brass wagon," or "Swing on the tire, old brass wagon." If she doesn't volunteer any observations, sing some of your own.

Large movement: Think up other ways to move: "Swing your arm, old brass wagon," or "Wiggle your hips, old brass wagon." Try anything your children or their playmates offer.

History: "Old Brass Wagon" is an old square dance tune, popular in pioneer times.

Recording: Piano, guitar, bass, violin, tambourine, tone block, cowbell

Ride-O

Traditional, arranged and
adapted with new words by
K. Guilmartin and L. Levinowitz

VERSE
Bouncy

1, 2. *(sing on "doo," "dee," or any other syllable)*
3. Dri - ving, dri - ving, dri - ving, *etc.*
4. Zoom, zoom, zoom, zoom, zoom, zoom! *etc.*
5. Ti - ckle, ti - ckle, ti - ckle, *etc.*
6. La, la, la, la, la, la, *etc.*

Fine

(To INTERLUDE after verses 2, 4 and 6)

INTERLUDE

Voices: *(sing on "la")*

To VERSE

Instruments:

Let's go for a ride!

Seat your child next to you or on your lap and say, "Let's go for a ride!" Sing on "doo," "dee," or another syllable and move rhythmically as if riding horses or driving cars, trucks, bicycles, etc.

Claps 'n' taps: Clap your hands, or tap parts of your body such as your legs, head, shoulders, nose, etc. Take turns leading this tapping play. Put young children on your lap and bounce, tap, or tickle.

Vocal play: Sing using silly or unusual sounds like "buzz," "ding," or "waah" (crying sound). Sing in a deep, loud voice on "ho, ho, ho," and in a high, squeaky voice on "hee, hee, hee."

Infants and toddlers: Try singing this song as you go about your daily activities. For example, after a bath you can sing and move the towel rhythmically as you dry your child, using "la," "da," or one of your child's favorite sounds. Or sing about your child as he practices new physical skills: "rolling," "crawling," "waving," and "walking."

Older children: Vary the loudness and tempo to suit your child's favorite ways of moving. For example, you might do a brisk "marching" for one repetition, then a slower, quieter "sleeping" verse, followed by a loud and fast "chasing" verse. Ask them for ideas and whether they want a turn being the leader.

Recording: Guitar, bass, flute, shaker, woodblock, triangle

16

Round Robin

Rebecca Frezza

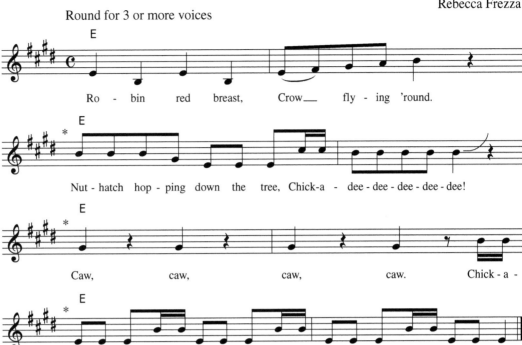

Round for 3 or more voices

Ro - bin red breast, Crow___ fly - ing 'round.

Nut - hatch hop - ping down the tree, Chick-a - dee - dee - dee - dee - dee!

Caw, caw, caw, caw. Chick - a -

dee - dee - dee, Chick - a - dee - dee - dee, Chick - a - dee - dee - dee, Chick - a - dee - dee - dee.

To create a round, additional voices can begin singing when the first voice reaches the asterisk (*).

Use your hand to create a bird, swooping it through the air or moving your thumb and fingers like a beak. Make some bird sounds, then create movements as you begin to sing:

Robin: Open and close your bird "beak" on the beat.
Crow: Make your hand flat like a wing and "fly" it to and fro in the air.
Nuthatch: Bounce your hand lightly in the air to mime a bird "hopping down the tree."
Chickadee: Open and close your beak rapidly on each "dee," moving your hand upward
along with the vocal swoop on the last "dee."

Round: Divide the available singers into two or more groups and decide who will go first, second, and so on. Begin by singing the song all together once or twice; then have the first group begin the round. When the first group reaches the first asterisk in the music above, the second group comes in. Sing in two parts at first, then in three or four as your confidence grows— along with the fun!

Storybook time: Use the songbook as a storybook and point rhythmically to each bird as you sing about it.

Tingalayo

Traditional, arranged and
adapted by K. Guilmartin
Spanish words by Gerry Dignan

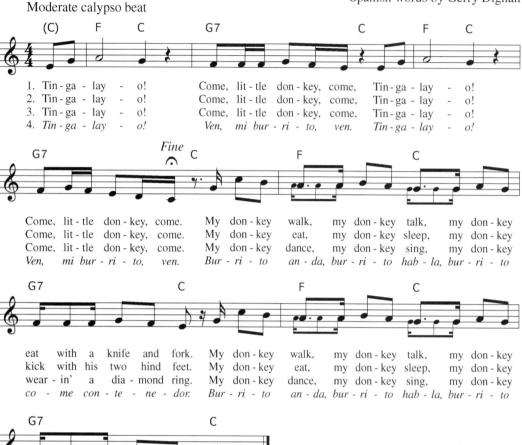

Moderate calypso beat

1. Tin - ga - lay - o!   Come, lit - tle don - key, come,   Tin - ga - lay - o!
2. Tin - ga - lay - o!   Come, lit - tle don - key, come,   Tin - ga - lay - o!
3. Tin - ga - lay - o!   Come, lit - tle don - key, come,   Tin - ga - lay - o!
4. *Tin - ga - lay - o!   Ven, mi bur - ri - to, ven.   Tin - ga - lay - o!*

Fine

Come, lit - tle don - key, come.   My don - key walk,   my don - key talk,   my don - key
Come, lit - tle don - key, come.   My don - key eat,   my don - key sleep,   my don - key
Come, lit - tle don - key, come.   My don - key dance,   my don - key sing,   my don - key
Ven, mi bur - ri - to, ven.   Bur - ri - to an - da,   bur - ri - to hab - la,   bur - ri - to

eat with a knife and fork.   My don - key walk,   my don - key talk,   my don - key
kick with his two hind feet.   My don - key eat,   my don - key sleep,   my don - key
wear - in' a dia - mond ring.   My don - key dance,   my don - key sing,   my don - key
co - me con - te - ne - dor.   Bur - ri - to an - da,   bur - ri - to hab - la,   bur - ri - to

eat with a knife and fork.
kick with his two hind feet.
wear - in' a dia - mond ring.
co - me con - te - ne - dor. (D.C. al Fine)

**Dance and sing
with the West
Indian donkey wh[o]
can do everything
people do!**

Pick up your baby, toddle with your toddler, or dance with your older child. Step to the beat, moving in a circle or winding your way through the house. Play some rattles, shakers, maracas, or a guiro as you dance and sing.

Variations: Try using your child's name instead of "Tingalayo" ("Tommy, Tommy! Dance, little Tommy, dance," or "Jenny, Jenny! Come, little Jenny, come.") Or try variations: "My Gerry walk, my Gerry talk, my Gerry eat with a cup and spoon."

Infants and toddlers: Put your baby on your hip and step to the basic beat, letting your body dip and sway easily with the music. Move from room to room, dancing playfully as you go. Stop at every mirror and let him see you both moving to the music. Lift him up high on the "Tingalayo" refrain, and then dance on the verses. When you're ready to stop, lay him down and tap his body gently to the beat as you sing the song quietly a few more times.

Recording: Guitar, bass, shakers, bongos, guiro

Betty Martin

Traditional, arranged and
adapted by K. Guilmartin

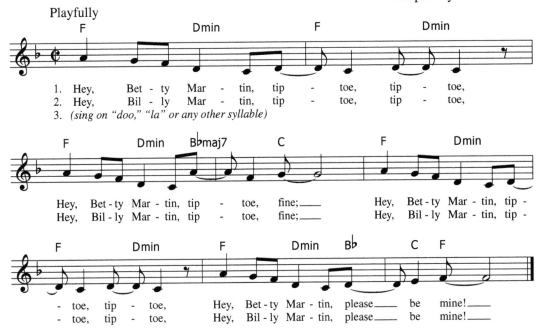

Tiptoe as you sing, or "tiptoe" with your fingers on your child's body. End with a tickle or a hug on the word "mine."

Variations: Sing your child's name instead of "Betty Martin." Substitute your name and other names, including family pets. You can even make a whole verse using just a name: "Hey, Joey, Joey, Joey, Joey, Hey, Joey, Joey, Joey, Joe," etc.

Another way to vary the song is to change the movement. Use one of your child's favorite ways to move: "Hey, Jenny Johnson, run around, run around, Hey, Jenny Johnson, run around time," etc. Repeat the movements with your child as you sing another verse on "doo" or another syllable.

Improvisation: On the recording you will hear the father's and child's voices improvise with the guitar and bass. You can try this, too. Sing on a syllable like "doo" and join in with the melody, but sing different rhythms. When you find a note that you like, keep repeating it until it sounds like you should change it. Improvisation is natural for children because it is musical play.

Recording: Guitar, bass, shakers, conga drums, triangle

One Little Owl

Traditional, arranged and adapted
by K. Guilmartin and L. Levinowitz
Additional words by K. Guilmartin

Look!
What's up
in the tree?

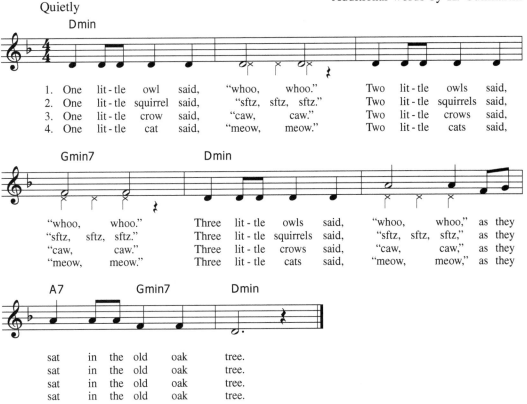

Quietly

Dmin

1. One lit-tle owl said, "whoo, whoo." Two lit-tle owls said,
2. One lit-tle squirrel said, "sftz, sftz, sftz." Two lit-tle squirrels said,
3. One lit-tle crow said, "caw, caw." Two lit-tle crows said,
4. One lit-tle cat said, "meow, meow." Two lit-tle cats said,

Gmin7   Dmin

"whoo, whoo." Three lit-tle owls said, "whoo, whoo," as they
"sftz, sftz, sftz." Three lit-tle squirrels said, "sftz, sftz, sftz," as they
"caw, caw." Three lit-tle crows said, "caw, caw," as they
"meow, meow." Three lit-tle cats said, "meow, meow," as they

A7   Gmin7   Dmin

sat in the old oak tree.
sat in the old oak tree.
sat in the old oak tree.
sat in the old oak tree.

Additional verses:

5. One big mom-my said, "Hold on tight!" (*grab an imaginary branch*)
Two big dad-dies said, "Hold on tight!" (*grab an imaginary branch*)
Three big pa-rents said, "Hold on tight!" (*grab an imaginary branch*)
As they sat in the old oak tree.

6. And the poor old tree said, "Oh, no!" (*raise arms like branches with palms up*)
And the poor old tree said, . . . *etc.* . . . . "All these things are sit-ting on me!"

Do characteristic movements for each animal or object as you sing about it:

Owl: Make circles with your thumb and index fingers and peer through your "owl eyes."
Squirrel: Hold your hands up like squirrel "paws" in front of your chest as you chatter.
Crow: Spread your arms out and flap them like wings.
Cat: Rub your "paw" along your cheek, or stretch out on hands and knees.
Oak tree: Spread your arms wide, as if they were branches.

Variations: Ask your child what else could be in the tree and what kind of sound it would make. Accept anything she suggests and sing playfully with her, making the movements of the chosen animals, machines, or other objects as best as you can. Be prepared for cows, dinosaurs, and back-hoes sitting in the tree!

Recording: Guitar, bass, bass recorder, wooden flute, ocarina, guiro, finger cymbals

Green and Blue

With delight

K. Guilmartin

Smells so green and skies so blue, Spring has sprung and now, me, too!

Boing, boing, boing, boing, boing, boing, boing, boing! Take off your mit-tens and

put a-way those coats, It's time for gar-dens and sail-ing in boats.

Smells so green and skies so blue, Spring has sprung, now how 'bout you?

f

Boing, boing, boing, boing, boing, boing, boing, boing!

Celebrate the smells, the colors —and the rhythms!— of spring.

Think spring, imagine being a child again, take a big breath of fresh air, and say the chant. Make up simple movements to go with the words. For example:

"Smells so green": Gesture with your hands as if smelling a bouquet of flowers, then make a similar, larger gesture to the sky.

"Spring has sprung": Make your hands jump on "sprung," then tap your chest on "me, too!"

"Boing, boing": Bounce your hands in the air as if they were flowers popping up out of the ground here, there, everywhere!

"Take off those mittens": Mime the actions.

"It's time for gardens": "Dig" in the garden and "sail" your hand over the waves.

"Spring has sprung, now how 'bout you?": As above, make your hands jump on "sprung," then gesture to your child or pick her up. Bounce your hands higher and higher on the "boing" sounds, or get up and jump!

Rhythm: The triple-meter rhythm feels like a waltz, with three small beats for every large one. You can experience this if you sway or rock as you speak the words, shifting your weight from one foot to the other.

Hey Ya Na

Traditional
Native American (Apache)

With a strong beat

Hey ya na,   Hey ya na,   O ha— le ya na ya.

Hey ya hey ya,   Hey— ya na,   O ha— le ya na ya.

Dance as you sing, connecting through your feet to the earth. Native American dancing emphasizes this connection, so bend over slightly at the waist, and focus more on the movement in your feet and legs than in your arms, torso, or head.

Large movement: The drums on the recording beat in a classic "heartbeat" pattern: strong-weak, strong-weak. Keep this feeling as you try some types of Native American dance steps. For example, walk deliberately, placing your toe on the floor on the strong beat, then lower the heel to the floor on the weak beat. Or move sideways, to the right, step-close, step-close. As your dancing becomes more confident, try some dancing spins: hop on one foot while twirling around in a small circle. For all of these steps, keep your arms loose and your body bent slightly toward the earth.

Instrument play: Get out your percussion instruments and play. Rattles, maracas, drums, jingle bells, and shakers all go well with this song. Some of the family can play drums while others dance; then switch.

Note: The words in "Hey Ya Na" have no literal meaning. They are neutral syllables or "vocables" chosen for their sound and rhythmic qualities.

Recording: Drums, shakers, bells

See the Pony Galloping

Traditional, arranged
by K. Guilmartin

INTRO
At a gallop!

continues *sim.*

VERSE

See the po - ny gal - lop - ing, gal - lop - ing, down the coun - try lane!

Gradually slower and quieter

lane! See the po - ny com - ing home, all tired out,

all tired out, all tired out.

Pretend to be a pony enjoying the sounds and rhythms of galloping—until you fall asleep!

You can start by sitting with your child on your lap, bouncing him to the beat of the music. Make "clip-clop" sounds by clucking your tongue in the galloping rhythm of the song; then sing. As the music slows down, lie down together to "sleep" for a minute, then sit up suddenly, perhaps with a "neigh," and start all over again. You can also get up and gallop around the room or yard.

Variations: Hold a toy horse or stuffed animal and make it "gallop" as you whinny and sing. Use your full vocal range to play with the animal sounds. When you see a pony—in a pasture, on TV, or in a book—try singing this song.

Note: This song is playful and full of contrasts. It also provides important musical experiences: *ritardando* (slowing down), *diminuendo* (getting quiet), and *sforzando* (being suddenly loud).

Recording: Guitar, bass, harmonica, wood block

Wedding Dance

Traditional, arranged and
adapted by K. Guilmartin

Dance and sing to this klezmer-style arrangement of a Hasidic tune.

Ya da yat dat da, Ya da da yat dat da, *(etc.)*

Sing and step to the beat of the music, accenting the strong beats by stomping into the floor. Gather everyone together and dance in a circle, moving to the right and left, in and out.

Infants: Lay your infant down so he can see you; then dance to the music, perhaps waving a colorful scarf. You can also help him feel the music by tapping his body in time and/or dancing with him.

Instrument play: Shake wrist bells lightly or wear them on wrists or ankles. Try leading with a tambourine, as Israeli folk dance leaders do; then pass the leadership to others by passing the tambourine.

Tonality: "Wedding Dance" is in a unique tonality called "Ahava Raba" which means "Love a lot." Music for weddings and bar mitzvahs is often written in this tonality.

Recording: Guitar, bass, soprano sax, tambourine, drums

Tricks with Sticks

K. Guilmartin

For nifty tricks, pick up your sticks!

INTRO

With a beat

("scat" ad lib)

Choo   chik - ka   choo   chik - ka   choo   choo   choo   choo.

Boom   chik - ka   boom   chik - ka   boom   boom   boom.

Skit - tle - y - up - pa   doo - dah,   a - ding   dong   ding.

Scoob - a   doob - a   doob - a,   a - bing   bong   bing.

VERSE 1

E

Hey,   ev - 'ry - bod - y,   lis - ten to me,   watch real close and then you'll see

E

how   to   do some nif - ty   tricks,   pick up   your sticks   and   go   like   this:

CHORUS

E   A   E   A   E

Ba da dum __ ba dum bum bum bum,   ba da dum __ ba dum dum.

E   A   A   E

ba   da dum __ ba dum bum bum bum,   ba da dum __ ba dum dum.

E   A   E   A   E

Ba   da dum __ ba dum bum bum bum,   ba da dum __ ba dum dum.

VERSE 2

E

Well,   How   do you do? and What a-bout that?   Bark goes the dog, me-ow goes the cat!

sing CHORUS

26

VERSE 3

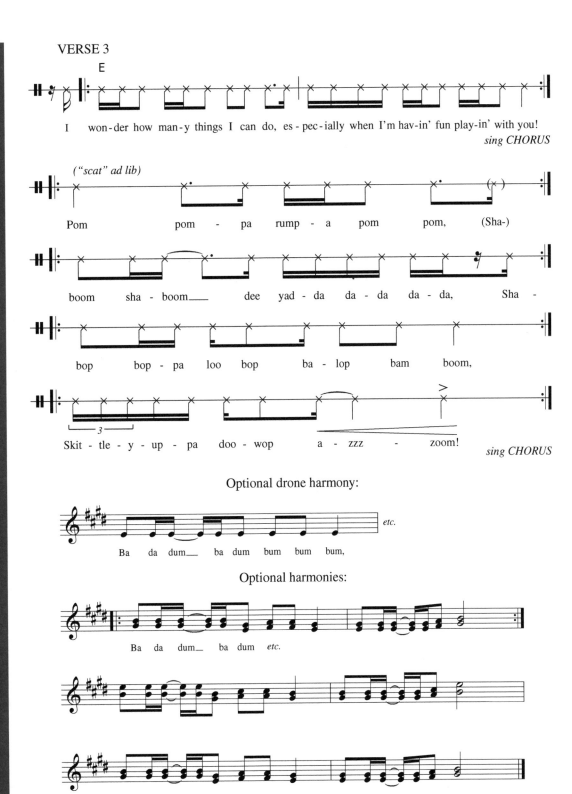

I won-der how man-y things I can do, es-pec-ial-ly when I'm hav-in' fun play-in' with you!

sing CHORUS

("scat" ad lib)

Pom pom - pa rump - a pom pom, (Sha-)

boom sha - boom___ dee yad - da da - da da - da, Sha -

bop bop - pa loo bop ba - lop bam boom,

Skit - tle - y - up - pa doo - wop a - zzz - zoom!

sing CHORUS

Optional drone harmony:

Ba da dum___ ba dum bum bum bum, *etc.*

Optional harmonies:

Ba da dum___ ba dum *etc.*

Get out the rhythm sticks, wooden spoons, or dowel rods and tap them to the beat.

Verse variations: Echo the scat lines as the singers do on the recording. Then use words or sounds to create your own short, silly phrases that can be echoed by others in your family.

Mouth music: Many cultures have some kind of "mouth music"—musical syllables that don't carry specific meaning. North American traditions include Native American chant, "doo-wop" (1950s rock 'n' roll), and the rhythmic syllables known in jazz as "scat."

Recording: Guitar, bass, conga drums, rhythm sticks, shaker, maracas, cowbell

Cradle Song

Words by William Blake
Music by K. Guilmartin

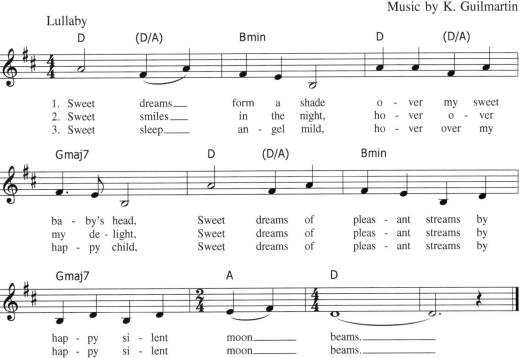

Lullaby

1. Sweet dreams form a shade o - ver my sweet
2. Sweet smiles in the night, ho - ver o - ver
3. Sweet sleep an - gel mild, ho - ver over my

ba - by's head, Sweet dreams of pleas - ant streams by
my de - light, Sweet dreams of pleas - ant streams by
hap - py child, Sweet dreams of pleas - ant streams by

hap - py si - lent moon beams.
hap - py si - lent moon beams.
hap - py si - lent moon beams.

Cuddle, rock, and sing of sweet dreams and moonbeams.

Sing or hum this lullaby when you want to help your child settle—at naptime, bedtime, riding on a plane, or when he's not feeling well. Sing gently, rocking and caressing him. With enough repetition, music has the power to soothe and quiet even the most active child. Invite an older child to join in as you sing to his pets or dolls.

Rocking chair and cradle: Rock and sing, moving gently in rhythm with the music. When it's time to put your child in bed, keep singing while you get her ready and tuck her in. Then sing or hum one more verse quietly, close to her, so she can sense your breathing and feel your voice.

Songbook illustration: Look at the illustration on the opposite page with your child. Who is the little girl rocking the cradle? Can you find another cradle in the picture? Many children are fascinated by the moon and stars. As you sing the song, point out the moon in the book or in the window.

Note: The words of this song are from *Songs of Innocence* (1789), a collection of poems and paintings by William Blake, an eighteenth-century poet.

Recording: Piano

Tambourine Jam

"Get your instrument and play along!"

K. Guilmartin

A high-point of Music Together classes is the jam session we call the "play-along."

In a play-along, everyone, infant to grandparent, chooses an instrument and plays along with a recording or with live musicians. Suggestion: Before you get out the instruments, try listening to the play-along a few times while you move or dance to the rhythms with your child.

Keep your own collection of real and "found" instruments handy in a drawer or basket, so you can pull them out easily for a play-along—or get out the pots and pans! Everybody plays something. If you haven't touched that clarinet since high school or college, why not get it out and try? Your example of participation means so much more to your child than performing the "right notes."

As you become familiar with "Tambourine Jam," stop, start, and accent with the flow of the music. If you exaggerate these moments somewhat, even toddlers may notice and follow you! Just repeatedly set the example and see what happens.

This song is also good for dancing or free movement, or you may want to move and play an instrument at the same time. If children do this, just make sure the instrument is safe for movement.

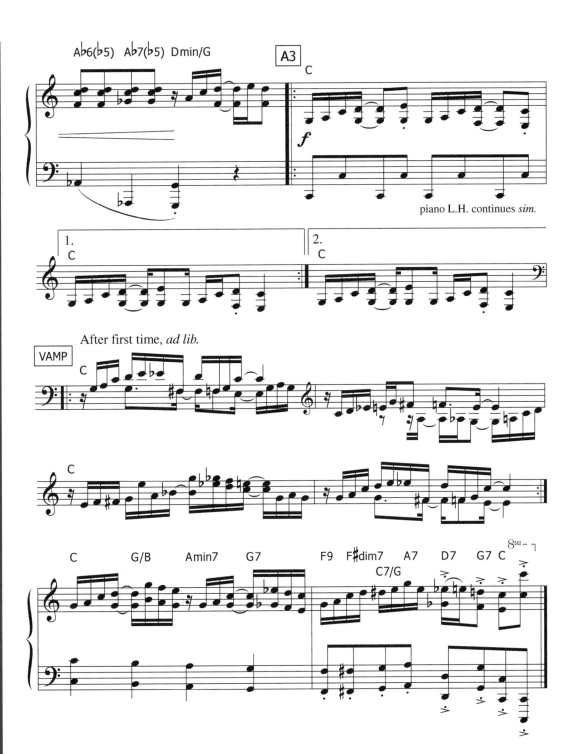

Note: The unusual tambourine-like sounds on the recording are made by a "rik," a Middle Eastern tambourine with large jingles. Rik performance techniques include playing patterns on the jingles as much as on the skin head.

Recording: Piano, guitar, bass, harmonica, drums, shakers, bodhran (Irish frame drum), rik

Sneakin' 'Round the Room

K. Guilmartin

Sneak, strut, waltz, and boogie in your living room!

Use the recording to learn the four basic movements and singing styles: sneak (quietly, with drama and suspense), walk (hip, cool, with attitude), dance (waltz, spin, sway), and boogie (jazzy).

Songbook illustration: Sing the tune in different ways for different people in the picture. For example, sing "doo" for the girl on her knees and "waaah" for the baby. Sing in a deeper voice for the dad, a scary voice for the big girl, and very quietly for the boy hiding behind the chair.

Note: The fermatas (⌒) in the music indicate when to "hold" the notes to build suspense. It's also fun to "freeze" your movement while you hold your singing note on each of the fermatas.

Recording: Piano, bass, pennywhistle, drums

Hippity, Happity, Hoppity

Doug Morris

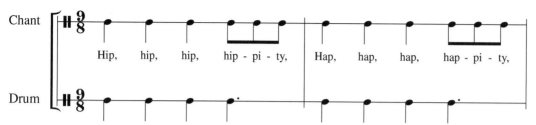

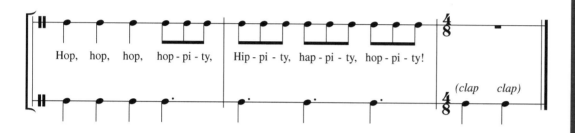

Clap 'n' tap along with the snazzy, jazzy rhythm of this chant.

Get to know this interesting rhythm by saying the chant along with the recording as you move with your child in rhythmic ways. After a while you'll find yourself spontaneously thinking or saying the chant without the help of the recording!

Rhythm note: Most music in Western culture tends to group either two or three beats together, creating what we call either duple meter (like a march) or triple meter (like a waltz). This chant, however, combines groups of two *and* three beats together in one phrase, providing a wonderful sense of drive. Each phrase contains nine microbeats, grouped into pulses of twos and threes as follows:

1-2 **1**-2 **1**-2 **1** - 2 - 3   **1**-2 **1**-2 **1**-2 **1** - 2 - 3   **1**-2 **1**-2 **1**-2 **1** - 2 - 3
Hip, hip, hip, hip-pi-ty,   **Hap, hap, hap, hap**-pi-ty,   **Hop, hop, hop, hop**-pi-ty,

1 - 2 - 3 **1** - 2 - 3 **1** - 2 - 3   **1**-2   **1**-2
Hip-pi-ty, **hap**-pi-ty, **hop**-pi-ty! (clap) (clap)

Try putting this unequal rhythm into your body by tapping your legs on the short (duple) beats, and tapping your head on the long (triple) beats: leg-leg-leg-head, leg-leg-leg-head. You can also try tapping on the twos and making a circular motion on the threes to illustrate the different size beats. This kind of uneven grouping is common in world music, but some Western adults may find it unusual or challenging at first. For a child, early experience with a chant like "Hippity, Happity, Hoppity" will make this kind of rhythm as accessible as any other and will expand her rhythmic vocabulary.

Recording: Claves, shakers

Pawpaw Patch

Traditional, arranged and
adapted by K. Guilmartin

Brightly

1. Where, oh where, oh where is Su-sie? Where, oh where, oh where is Su-sie?
2. Come on kids, let's go find her, Come on kids, let's go find her,

Where, oh where, oh where is Su-sie? Way down yon-der in the paw-paw patch.
Come on kids, let's go find her, Way down yon-der in the paw-paw patch.

3. Pick-in' up paw-paws, put 'em in your pock-et, Pick-in' up paw-paws,

put 'em in your pock-et, Pick-in' up paw-paws, put 'em in your pock-et,

D.C. al Fine

Way down yon-der in the paw-paw patch.

Where's Susie?
Let's go find her!

Act out the song by moving rhythmically with motions that suit the words. Pretend to shield your eyes from the sun as you search for "Susie," point (on the beat) to an imaginary pawpaw patch, gesture for the "kids" to come along, and end by happily picking pawpaws.

Variations: Sing when something's lost—"Where, oh where, oh where are my car keys?" and "Come on, Paul, help me find them."

Hide-and-seek: Young children love games of hide-and-seek. Everyone takes turns hiding while the rest of the family sings, "Where, oh where, oh where is ____," and so on. If younger children want company hiding, fit two names to the tune!

Infants and toddlers: Hide something small, like a rattle, under a blanket while your baby watches. Sing, "Where, oh where, oh where's the rattle?" Then pull it out and sing, "Here, oh here, oh here's the rattle," shaking it to the beat as you sing. Hide the rattle and sing again, and see what happens.

History: A pawpaw is a large fruit that looks like a mango and grows on trees with big, droopy, tropical-looking leaves. It tastes like banana-strawberry custard and is found in twenty-six states.

Recording: Guitar, bass, tambourine

Merry-Go-Round

Lynn Lobban

1. Mer-ry-go-round, mer-ry-go-round, a-round and a-round and a-round. Mer-ry-go-round, mer-ry-go-round, a-round and a-round and a-round. The hors-es go up and then they go down, a-round and a-round and a-round. The hors-es go up and then they go down, a-round and a-round and a-round.

2. Diz-zy go 'round, diz-zy go 'round, a-round and a-round and a-round. Diz-zy go 'round, diz-zy go 'round, a-round and a-round and a-round. I ride the horse up and ride the horse down, a-round and a-round and a-round. I ride the horse up and ride the horse down, a-round and a-round and a-round.

3. Mer-ry-go-round, mer-ry-go-round, a-round and a-round and a-round. Mer-ry-go-round, mer-ry-go-round, a-round and a-round and a-round.

(D.C. al Coda)

round and a-round and a-round and a-round and a-round!

Move your arms in a circle in time to the music as you sing this song. When you sing about the horses going up and down, try lifting up and lowering your child. You can even move around the room as if you were horses on a merry-go-round, moving up and down as you circle around.

Songbook illustration: Look at the illustration on the opposite page as you sing the song with your child. Hold the last note (the "resting tone") and *sing* some questions to her on this note. For example, "What is the little boy doing?" or "What do you see in the picture on the wall?"

Recording: Guitar, bass, MIDI calliope, wood block, bell tree

Secrets

Linda Betlejeski, K. Guilmartin
and L. Levinowitz

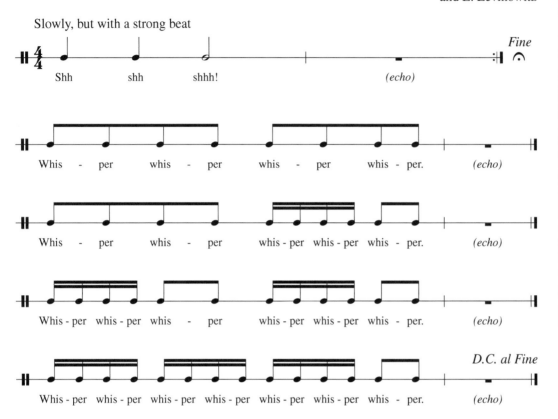

Slowly, but with a strong beat

Shh   shh   shhh!   (echo)

Whis - per   whis - per   whis - per   whis - per.   (echo)

Whis - per   whis - per   whis-per whis-per whis - per.   (echo)

Whis-per whis-per whis - per   whis-per whis-per whis - per.   (echo)

D.C. al Fine

Whis-per whis-per whis-per whis-per whis-per whis-per whis - per.   (echo)

Shhhhh!
I've got a secret.

Sit close and whisper the chant to your child. (Be sure you start slowly enough to be able to say the last line!) After they have learned it, older children may be able to answer with the echo (as heard on the CD). If your child is younger, model the echo with the help of an older child or another adult, or simply repeat each phrase in an even quieter voice.

Variations: First become comfortable with the form of this chant: a phrase followed by its echo, then a different phrase followed by its echo. Then make up a new phrase and whisper it rhythmically in a hushed voice. Try using two-syllable words like "se-cret" or "e-cho." Try words that are especially interesting or exciting for your child: "pre-sent" or "ice cream." Use this chant the next time you want to tell your child about a special surprise.

Rhythm note: This song provides a structured experience of different levels of beat, especially macrobeat (the basic beat), microbeat (twice as fast), and the next level of diminution (four times as fast). See the glossary for definitions of macrobeat and microbeat.

Rhythm development: Children benefit from hearing the chant many times and freely experimenting with saying it their way, even if that differs from the "correct" version. When your child's development allows her to echo each phrase, it will be interesting for you to see if she keeps a steady beat, even though the words get very fast. When she can keep the beat steadily throughout and echo patterns accurately, she has probably achieved basic rhythm competence.

Ding Dong, Ding Dong

Traditional, arranged and adapted by
K. Guilmartin and L. Levinowitz

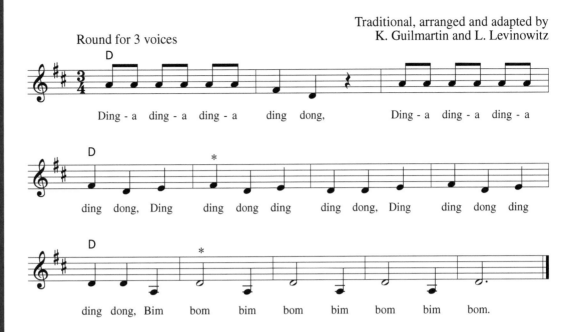

Round for 3 voices

Ding - a ding - a ding - a ding dong, Ding - a ding - a ding - a

ding dong, Ding ding dong ding ding dong, Ding ding dong ding

ding dong, Bim bom bim bom bim bom bim bom.

To create a round, additional voices can begin singing when the first voice reaches the asterisk (*).

Sing and sway to the macrobeat, following the three-beat feel of the music. The tempo and feel match the way children rock back and forth, shifting their weight naturally from one foot to the other.

Singing a round: When your family knows the song well, divide into two groups with some stronger singers in each group. One group starts the round, and the second group enters after one phrase, as indicated by the asterisks in the music and heard on the recording. This can be especially rewarding for older children or adults who may discover they can "hold their own part" for the first time; but remember that getting "lost" is all part of the fun! For a three-part round, a third group enters after group two sings the first phrase.

Bell play: Play along with any bells you can find—jingle bells, school bells, bells on charm bracelets—as well as objects with ringing, bell-like, metallic sounds—full key rings or kitchen equipment. For some children, this concrete expression of bells will be fascinating. Another day, pretend to ring imaginary hand bells or pull on a big rope to ring a cathedral bell.

Learning rhythm: It is important for young children to experience rhythm through movement, so instead of just singing this song, move to it as well. This can help your child establish a strong sense of pulse during the years when he can develop this most easily.

Recording: Celesta

This 'n' That

K. Guilmartin

Cuban feel

1, 6. Na na na___ na na, Na na na___ na na.
2. Dance with me___ like this, Dance with me___ like that.
3. *Va - mos a bai - lar a - sí,* *Va - mos a bai - lar a - sí.*
4. Move your hips___ like this, Move your hips___ like that.
5. Can you go___ like this? Can you go___ like that?
7. Sing a song___ like this, Sing a song___ like that.
8. *Va - mos a can - tar a - sí,* *Va - mos a can - tar a - sí.*

Na na na___ na na, Na na na___ na na.
Dance with me___ like this, Dance with me___ like that.
Va - mos a bai - lar a - sí, *Va - mos a bai - lar a - sí.*
Move your hips___ like this, Move your hips___ like that. *(to Interlude)*
We can go___ like this. We can go___ like that.
Sing a song___ like this, Sing a song___ like that.
Va - mos a can - tar a - sí, *Va - mos a can - tar a - sí.* *(to Interlude)*

INTERLUDE
(After verse 8, vamp *ad lib. al Fine*)

(sing on "la")

Fine

Join in on the dancing fun!

Make up movements or just let loose and dance the mambo! Carry little ones or simply let them watch. Everyone sings the "na na" or "la la" verses. Then try doing the following kinds of interactions:

Dance with me like this: Leader models contrasting movements (right/left, up/down, slow/fast).
Move your hips like this: Find different ways to move your hips, or move other parts of your body such as your arms or shoulders.
Can you go like this: Leader models and followers sing "we can go like this" as they do it.
Sing a song like this (*): At the asterisks, followers answer by singing "na, na, na" as on the recording, perhaps using some of the harmonies presented.

Spanish translation: *Vamos a bailar asi* means "let's dance like this." Similarly, *vamos a cantar asi* means "let's sing like this." In Spanish, there is no difference between the words "this" and "that."

Recording: Piano, bass, conga drums, timbales, cowbell, claves

Scarborough Fair

Traditional, arranged
by K. Guilmartin

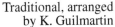

A favorite of many generations— pass it along to your children.

Rhythmic movement helps children connect with slow, quiet music. Sway and sing while you hold your child close, moving your whole torso so she will feel you move and breathe.

Large movement: Toddlers can stand on your feet as you rock side-to-side. Older children can rock independently or sway with a partner (dolls or stuffed animals can also be partners). Get out scarves or pieces of cloth, and let them flow with you as you move to the music, using your whole body.

Singing in harmony: If you enjoy singing harmony, try singing the harmony heard on the last verse of the recording. You can learn it by singing along with the CD or by reading the small cue notes in the music. You can also create a simple drone (a held or repeated note) harmony by singing the resting tone (B, the song's first note) all the way through the song, while someone else sings the melody. Note the lovely dissonance on the word "there."

Lullaby: Sing this familiar folk song to your child as he settles for sleep.

Guitar: Guitarists may find it easier to put the capo on the second fret and play in A minor.

Recording: Guitar, bass, pennywhistle

Good News

Traditional African-American spiritual, arranged with additional lyrics by K. Guilmartin

With a beat (♩♩ = ♩ ♪)

1. Good news! Char-i-ot's a-com-in', ___ Good news!
2. *(sing on "doo")*
3. Beep! Beep! Bus___ is a-com-in', ___ *etc.*
4. Toot! Toot! Train___ is a-com-in', ___ *etc.*

Char-i-ot's a-com-in', ___ Good news! Char-i-ot's a-com-in', ___

1. - 3.
Fine

4.

don't leave me be - hind. hind.

(optional: sing melody on "doo")

Choo choo choo choo choo choo choo choo *etc.*

D.C. al Fine

Sing the song as written, moving around the room as if you were on a chariot, bus, or train. People of all ages can enjoy making train sounds, forming a train, and following the leader around the house.

Traveling: Older children will enjoy singing about different ways they travel—car, train, plane, trucks, and boats. Imaginary travel could be fun, too—pterodactyl, magic carpet, space ship, fire truck, etc.

Singing in harmony: Sing the "choo-choo" vocal harmony that follows the train verse. Learn it by singing along with the singers on the recording; then sing it without the recording.

Recording: Guitar, bass, harmonica, drums, tambourine

Raisins and Almonds

Traditional Yiddish folk song,
arranged by K. Guilmartin

Lullaby

To my lit - tle one's cra - dle in the night comes a lit - tle goat snow - y and

white. The goat will trot to the mar - ket,_____ while

moth - er her watch__ does keep, bring - ing back rai - sins and al - monds.__

1. Sleep, my lit - tle one, sleep.____

2. Sleep, my lit - tle one, sleep.

A rich and warm traditional melody brings sweet dreams.

This is a lovely tune to sing anytime, anywhere, but it is especially fine as a lullaby. Standing, or rocking in a chair, sway gently back and forth to the beat as you sing "to Elizabeth's cradle" or "to my little John's cradle." Adapt the words and rhythm to your child's name; then hum the melody or sing on "la," "noo," or another syllable.

Infants: Sing to your infant in a relaxed way. If you leave a little silence between repetitions and if your child is vocal, she may spontaneously make her own "lullaby" sounds. Imitate the sounds she makes, then change them slightly and see her response. She may change her sounds, too, or may just listen.

Songbook: Make music part of your ritual before bedtime or naptime by using the songbook as a storybook. Page through the book together, looking at the pictures and singing a little bit of each song you know. Your model will help your child want to learn to sing and read music books, too.

When grandparents, babysitters, and other caregivers put your child to bed, give them the book and ask them to follow your bedtime ritual. After a while, your older child may want to page through the book on his own, singing the song or parts of the songs to himself. Children may also enjoy paging through the book while listening to the CD—the book's song order follows the CD song order, and this lovely song is at the end.

Recording: Guitar, bass

Goodbye, So Long, Farewell

K. Guilmartin

When it's time to say goodbye to children or friends, try singing this song. It's a good reminder that you'll see each other again soon!

Jazz waltz

1. Good - bye, so long, fare - well, my friends, good -
2. Good - bye to *(name)*, good - bye to *(different name)*, good -
3. Good - bye, so long, fare - well, my friends, good -

bye, so long, fare - well. We'll see you
bye, so long, fare - well. Good - bye to
bye, so long, fare - well. We'll see you

soon a - gain, my friends, so good - bye, so
ev - 'ry - bo - dy here,_____ good - bye, so
soon a - gain, and then we'll make Mu - sic To -

1. 2. / **3.** Slower

long, fare - well.
long, fare - well.
ge - ther a - gain.

And how 'bout a

hug for your mom or dad, or the one who takes

care of you? And a hug or a hand - shake for your

friends, and then how 'bout one just for your - self, too?

Sing the name of your child, holding younger ones and swaying to the waltz beat. You can also evoke the feeling of the song by just humming it or singing it on "la" or "doo." When you and your child must separate for a time, this song may be very helpful. Sing it before you leave the room, returning with the "Hello Song." Or try it while walking your child to the preschool door. The rhythm and tempo of the song make it especially appealing—walking could turn into skipping or dancing!

Recording: Piano, bass, shaker, triangle

MUSICAL MEMORIES

MUSICAL MEMORIES

GLOSSARY

Audiation. "Hearing" music when it is not physically present—the mental process allowing a person to "think" music and create it.

Basic music competence. The ability to sing in tune and move with accurate rhythm. While many children in our culture can develop this inborn potential by the age of five or six, kindergarteners with little music experience often cannot sing in tune or move to a beat. With a sufficiently rich music environment, however, a child can do so as early as age three or four.

Beat. Music's basic pulse. The main beat that most people would naturally tap to a song. We call this consensus beat the *macrobeat*.

Downbeat. The first, slightly stronger beat in a music measure.

Drone. A tone or pitch, usually a resting tone or related note, that is sustained or repeated throughout a long section of music, regardless of the shifting harmonic relationships that may occur.

Harmony. Two or more notes sounding together, thus creating a pleasing or interesting sound.

Macrobeat. What most listeners would agree is the basic pulse of a song. It is the main,"big" beat, in contrast to the smaller *microbeat*.

Measure. A group of macrobeats (usually from two to four) with the first beat slightly accented. In music notation, each measure is enclosed by vertical lines called bar lines.

Meter. Beats are usually grouped in recurring pulses of twos or threes, creating what we call either duple meter (like a march) or triple meter (like a waltz), with the first note of each group slightly accented. Some songs have a pulse which combines groups of two *and* three beats within a single phrase, resulting in an asymmetrical or "unusual" meter. Songs that have duple or compound notation but are triple at the microbeat level are said to be in "swing" meter.

Microbeat. The first subdivision of the macrobeat or basic pulse of the music. This "small" beat is faster: two macrobeats per measure (duple meter) would become four microbeats when subdivided, while three macrobeats per measure (triple meter) would be subdivided into six microbeats.

Music achievement. What we are able to do with our natural aptitude for music. This includes singing in tune and moving with accurate rhythm, as well as learning to play an instrument, making up melodies, or improvising musically with friends and family.

Music aptitude. The inborn potential for music learning and growth. While this is determined biologically, as far as we know, it can also be influenced by the surrounding environment. Before the age of five, music aptitude is especially malleable: rich and varied music experience can help it develop, while lack of experience leads to atrophy. By the age of nine, as neurological pathways in the brain begin to mature, the child's music aptitude stabilizes.

Offbeats. Rather than accenting the downbeat (see above), certain types of music accent offbeats or "backbeats" for musical effect.

For example, gospel music often emphasizes clapping on beat 2 and 4.

Ostinato. A short musical phrase or pattern which can be repeated over and over again to accompany the rest of the song.

Play. The delightful way by which young children teach themselves: they observe, imitate, explore, experiment, practice, and create.

Primary music development. The period in a child's life when the developing brain is most open to musical influence and growth. During this time, the child moves through predictable, observable stages of music learning culminating in *basic music competence*. Exposure to a variety of music and movement experiences is crucial during this period, when the child learns so fast and so well.

Resting tone. The tonal note in a song where the music comes to "rest," usually the last note of the song. This note is also called "do," "1," and the "tonic."

Resting tone chord. The basic chord derived from a song, which includes the resting tone and the third and fifth notes above it. Sounding together, these three notes form a "chord" which most people find pleasing. Very young children often sound the resting tone or the fifth note spontaneously after hearing a song, an important first step in achieving tonal competence. This chord is also called the "tonic" or "1" chord.

Rhythm patterns. Short rhythmic phrases, generally based upon and directly following a song or chant in a Music Together class or recording. These patterns intentionally have no melodic component, in order to provide an experience of only the rhythmic aspect of music. Children learn by imitating these basic building blocks of rhythm and by making up some of their own.

Round. A song which goes "around" again. One voice (or group of voices) begins singing the melody followed by two to four other voices (or groups) singing the same melody but beginning at successively later times. The melody of the round is cleverly designed to "fit" harmonically, despite being out of phase with itself several times over.

S.Q. or Silly Quotient. A Music Together takeoff on I.Q. (intelligence quotient). Young children are very serious about being silly. It helps drive their interest in play, one of their primary learning strategies. Children respect authentic S.Q. in the adults around them, and a genuine grasp of it can increase a teacher's effectiveness in the classroom. It also creates more fun for everyone.

Tonal patterns. Groups of two or three notes, based upon and following a song just sung in a Music Together class or recording. The tones intentionally have no rhythmic component, in order to provide an experience of only the tonal aspect of music. Imitating and playing with tonal patterns can help children organize their musical thought so they can sing and create songs.

Vocables. Vocal sounds or syllables, such as "bom," "doo," or "la." When sung in melodies, they carry no semantic meaning but are integrated in sound and rhythm into the music.

GUITAR REFERENCE CHART

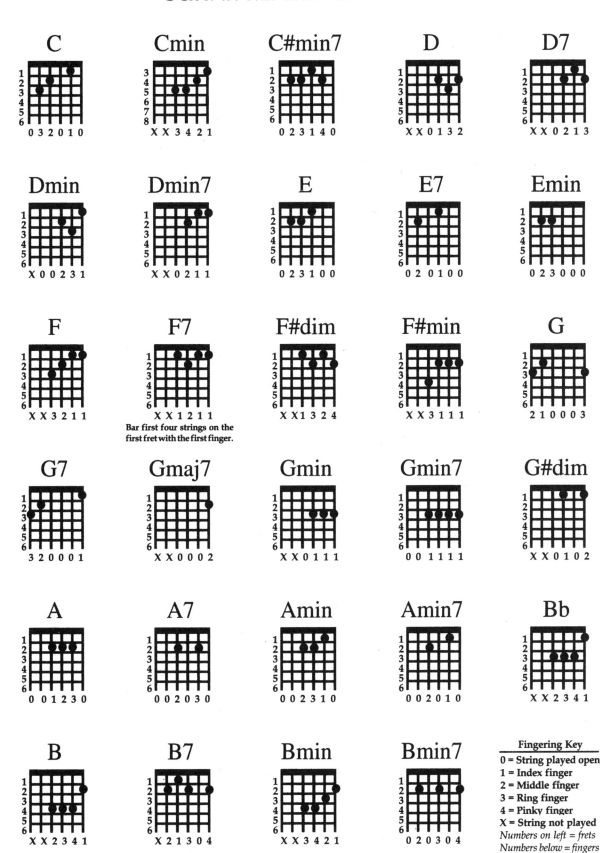

C
0 3 2 0 1 0

Cmin
X X 3 4 2 1

C#min7
0 2 3 1 4 0

D
X X 0 1 3 2

D7
X X 0 2 1 3

Dmin
X 0 0 2 3 1

Dmin7
X X 0 2 1 1

E
0 2 3 1 0 0

E7
0 2 0 1 0 0

Emin
0 2 3 0 0 0

F
X X 3 2 1 1

F7
X X 1 2 1 1

Bar first four strings on the
first fret with the first finger.

F#dim
X X 1 3 2 4

F#min
X X 3 1 1 1

G
2 1 0 0 0 3

G7
3 2 0 0 0 1

Gmaj7
X X 0 0 0 2

Gmin
X X 0 1 1 1

Gmin7
0 0 1 1 1 1

G#dim
X X 0 1 0 2

A
0 0 1 2 3 0

A7
0 0 2 0 3 0

Amin
0 0 2 3 1 0

Amin7
0 0 2 0 1 0

Bb
X X 2 3 4 1

B
X X 2 3 4 1

B7
X 2 1 3 0 4

Bmin
X X 3 4 2 1

Bmin7
0 2 0 3 0 4

Fingering Key

0 = String played open
1 = Index finger
2 = Middle finger
3 = Ring finger
4 = Pinky finger
X = String not played
Numbers on left = frets
Numbers below = fingers

REFERENCES

Gardner, Howard. *Multiple Intelligences: The Theory in Practice*. New York: BasicBooks, 1993.

Gordon, Edwin E. *A Music Learning Theory for Newborn and Young Children*. Chicago: GIA Publication, Inc., 1997.

Guilmartin, Kenneth K., and Lili M. Levinowitz. *Music and Your Child: A Guide for Parents and Caregivers*. Princeton, NJ: Center for Music and Young Children, 1989.

Holt, John. *How Children Learn*. New York: Dell Publishing Co., Inc., 1983.

Machover, Wilma, and Marienne Uszler. *Sound Choices: Guiding Your Child's Musical Experiences*. New York: Oxford University Press, Inc., 1996.

Pearce, Joseph Chilton. *Evolution's End: Claiming the Potential of Our Intelligence*. San Francisco: HarperSanFrancisco, 1992.

Pearce, Joseph Chilton. *Magical Child*. New York: Bantam Books, Inc., 1980.

ACKNOWLEDGMENTS

The authors would like to acknowledge the major sources of influence on the ongoing evolution of Music Together since it first began to take shape in the mid-eighties. The work of Emile Jaques-Dalcroze, particularly as interpreted by Robert M. Abramson, is fundamental to Ken Guilmartin's approach to music and movement education. Lili Levinowitz became inspired by the music learning theory of Edwin F. Gordon and worked with him closely as Director of the Children's Music Development program at Temple University, where she obtained her Ph.D. Both authors wish to acknowledge the ongoing research and creative field applications of their colleagues, and they are especially grateful for the feedback and inspirational enthusiasm of Music Together teachers, center directors, and families everywhere.

To create a truly developmentally appropriate program, the authors looked beyond music education to the field of early childhood education. Especially notable among many influences is Ken's eight-year experience with the Montclair Cooperative School as a parent and faculty member, and for both authors, the inspiration of parenting their own children, Eli Levinowitz and Lauren Guilmartin.

Finally, both authors wish to thank David K. Sengstack who provided both the initial vision and the means to begin this wonderful work.

TAMBOURINE Production Team—
Catherine Judd Hirsch, production editing
Susan Pujdak Hoffman, content editing
Marcel Chouteau, Jennifer Leach, production assistance
Music Together editorial review committee: Susan Darrow, Deanna deCampos, Susan Hoffman, Jackie Jacobs, Sally Woodson
Robert Bowen, music engraving
Main Street Design, logos and songbook design
Janet Payne, illustrations

Please feel free to contact us!

www.musictogether.com
(800) 728-2692